Emily
and the
Exuberant melody

BONNEY
PRESS

Published by Bonney Press,
an imprint of Hinkler Books Pty Ltd 2019
45–55 Fairchild Street
Heatherton Victoria 3202 Australia
www.hinkler.com

BONNEY
PRESS

Story by Katie Hewat
Biographies by Debra Thomas
Illustrations by Violetta Borigard

Editorial: Emily Murray
Design: Bianca Zuccolo
Publishing Manager: Jennifer Bilos
Prepress: Splitting Image

ISBN: 978 1 4889 7607 0

Printed and bound in China

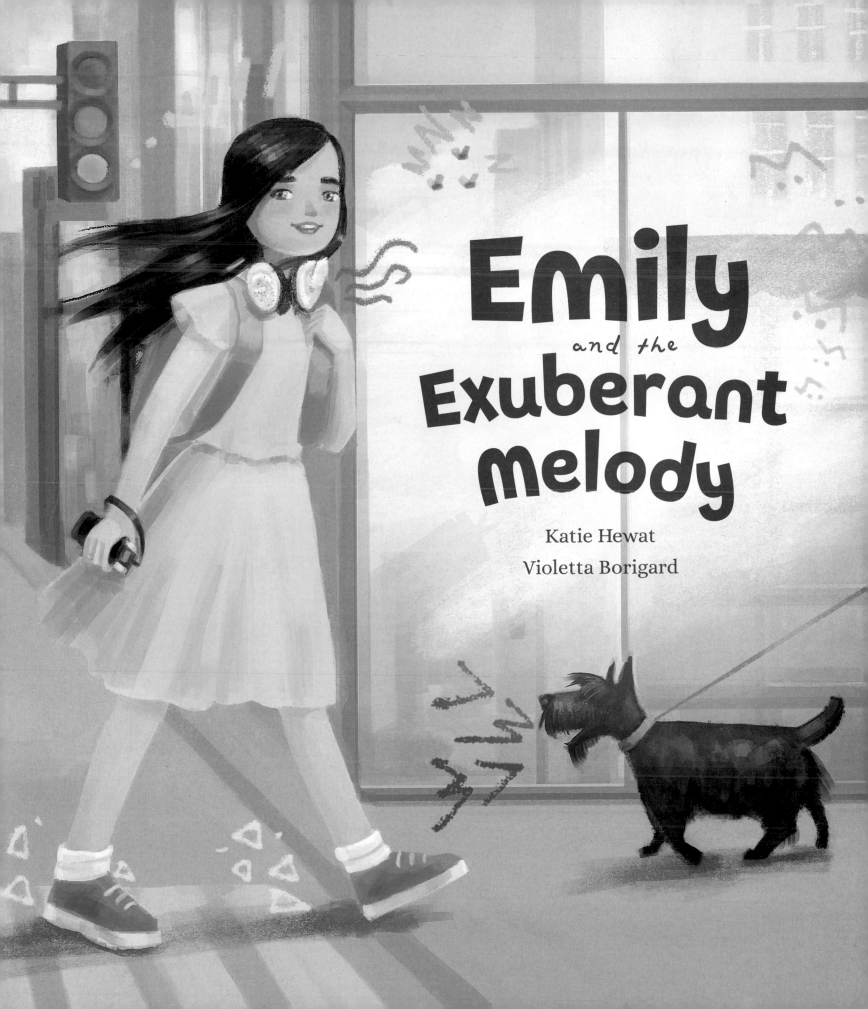

Emily
and the
Exuberant
melody

Katie Hewat

Violetta Borigard

Music is pure; it's golden and bright.
It flows all around me and makes me feel light.

I clap and I tap, I hum and I sing.
Arrangements surround me and burst from within.

At home it's the dishes and paws on the stairs,
the tick of the clock and the scraping of chairs.

When I'm outdoors it's the buzzing of bees,

the chirping of birds and the wind in the trees.

My Grandad's the same; he's exactly like me.
He hears tunes in the wind, in the birds and the bees.

Soft, smooth and sleepy or bold, loud and clappy;
whatever the tune, it makes him feel happy.

XI FESTIVAL

Concert

FOR GRANDMA'S BIRTHDAY

With Emily 2,5 YEARS

Today's song is sad as Grandad is poorly.
I know what to do and I'll need to move quickly!

I'll gather up sounds and make him a song,
and he'll have his groove back, before very long.

I head out of my house and down to the park,
where I capture some laughter and a dog's happy bark.

I skip past a builder who's
              sawing and banging,
                    whirring and tapping,
                          clinking and clanging.

I cross over the road hearing traffic lights ticking,
a man speaking German, a camera lens clicking.

There's a man at the station who's playing the sax
and the hoot of a train as it chugs down the tracks.

Down on the field, there's whistles and calls,
a big cheering crowd and the thwacking of balls.

The station alarm is flashing and ringing.
Engines are roaring and sirens are singing.

I love gathering sounds in the glorious weather,
but I have to get home and piece them together.

The tune's in my head but I need the right balance;
getting this right will take all of my talents!

I blend woofs, chugs and laughs, I splice bangs, taps and rings.
I throw in some clicks and a few other things.

Finally it happens; I know it's just right!

Now Grandad's song is ready; he can hear it tonight.

I'm at Grandad's home: he waits for me proudly.
A few of his friends start to clap and cheer loudly.

The music begins and the tune fills the air.
In the blink of an eye, Grandad's out of his chair!

He claps and he boogies,

he taps and he twists,

I knew he'd be happy, but nothing like this!

'I feel better already!'
he says as he dances.

He spins and he shimmies and actually prances!

Then he looks down at me with his twinkly eyes.

'Emily, my girl, that was such a surprise!'

'That's just what I need to get over my bug!'
He gives me a wink and a warm Grandad hug.

I'm so very happy, glad through and through,
that my passion for music brings others joy, too.

I knew it would happen; I knew I could do it!
  I'll *never* give up once I set my mind to it.

The Women Who Inspired Emily

Emily understood the power of music. Music can tell a story, provide comfort, entertain and, perhaps most inspiring of all, bring people together. Emily's gift to create a song that delighted her grandfather echoes the stories of the enormously talented women below. Despite the struggles they faced breaking into the male-dominated music industry, these women never gave up. Because of them, we all benefit from hearing their stories, being comforted by their voices, being entertained by their tunes – brought together by their greatness.

Francesca Caccini

18 SEPTEMBER 1587 – 1640 (DATE NOT AVAILABLE)
ITALY

Francesca was a gifted Italian musician in the sixteenth century. An enviable singer and composer, she could also play the lute, guitar, theorbo, harp and keyboard! Thought to be the composer of one of the very first operas, which was also the first opera by a woman, Francesca composed and performed music in the Medici court. Not only was she the most famous musician of her lifetime with over 32 songs and numerous operas to her name, she was the highest-paid musician in the Medici court. Although it is believed some of her work is mistakenly credited to her father Giulio, her one surviving full-length opera, *La Liberazione di Ruggiero dall'isola d'Alcina*, showcases her enormous skill and is still performed today.

Sister Rosetta Tharpe

'All this new stuff they call rock 'n' roll, why, I've been playing that for years now...'

20 MARCH 1915 – 9 OCTOBER 1973
UNITED STATES

Known as the 'Godmother of Rock 'n' Roll', Sister Rosetta was a gospel-singing, guitar-shredding musical prodigy. Fusing gospel music with blues and jazz, she became a powerhouse who broke through racial and musical barriers. Considered to be an originator of rock 'n' roll with her experimentation of form and guitar techniques, she was a powerful influence for many artists in the genre, including Elvis Presley, Johnny Cash and Bob Dylan. In 2018, Tharpe was finally inducted into the Rock & Roll Hall of Fame, with the Award for Early Influence.

Florence Price

9 APRIL 1887 – 3 JUNE 1953
UNITED STATES

First performing on the piano at just four years old, Florence composed over 300 pieces and was a gifted pianist. Although many of her pieces have been lost, her first symphony, Symphony in E minor, won the Rodman Wanamaker Competition in 1932 and went on to be performed by the Chicago Symphony Orchestra in 1933. It was the first symphony to be performed by an African-American woman.

Toshiko Akiyoshi

'I thought the Japanese fans and critics would really put me down [for my album Kogun] ... *so I was really surprised when that became a bestseller.'*

12 DECEMBER 1929 –
CHINA

Toshiko began learning the piano at just six years old, but after World War II, her parents couldn't afford a piano. Not letting that stand in her way, she kept playing by taking a gig as a pianist in a dancehall band. After attending the prestigious Berklee College of Music, she co-formed the Toshiko Akiyoshi Jazz Orchestra in 1973 to play her own compositions. Toshiko has 14 Grammy nominations to her name, as well as being named an NEA Jazz Master by the US National Endowment for the Arts.

Aretha Franklin

'I'm there to give the best performance I can. The idea is to be as uplifting as possible and as inspiring to people as possible.'

25 March 1942 – 16 August 2018
United States

Known as 'The Queen of Soul', Aretha had a vocal range almost twice the average, creating one of the most distinctive voices in music. Despite not knowing how to read music, Aretha taught herself how to play the piano, and she later studied classical piano at one of the most prestigious music schools in the world, the Juilliard School of Music. Aretha's fusion of R&B with jazz and pop redefined the pop genre, and in 1987 she became the first female performer to be inducted into the Rock & Roll Hall of Fame. With 41 studio albums and 18 Grammys to her name, Aretha Franklin was one of the most influential voices in pop history.

Björk Guðmundsdóttir

'I want to see what can be done with the entire emotional range of the human voice – a single voice, a chorus, trained voices, pop voices, folk voices, strange voices.'

21 November 1965 –
Iceland

Björk's music is full of imagination. Recording her first album when she was only 11, she has successfully worked as the lead singer of the Sugarcubes and has since produced nice solo albums. Björk has the power to completely reinvent herself and her sound with each new recording, often blending sounds and experimenting with everything from folk to opera. Known for her unique voice, which is often described as 'elfin' or 'celestial', Björk also has a captivating stage presence and is famous for her bold fashion choices. Never one to conform, her determination to stay true to herself has paid off, receiving more than 100 awards in just over 20 years in the music industry.

Joni Mitchell

'I wrote poetry, and I always wanted to make music. But I never put [them] together. Just a simple thing like being a singer-songwriter – that was a new idea.'

7 November 1943 –
Canada

At age nine, Joni contracted polio and was told she'd never walk again. Using music as therapy, Joni sang through the long nights in hospital until she had recovered. Falling in love with music, she began teaching herself guitar. With her left hand weakened from polio, she devised 50 unique ways to tune her guitar, which allowed her to play more freely. Joni's improvisation broke free of conventional songwriting and empowered her to become one of the most innovative and celebrated performers of her generation.

St. Vincent

'The strongest thing a woman can do is be successful, powerful and excel at whatever they choose to excel at.'

28 September 1982 –
United States

St. Vincent, born Annie Clark, has been described by *Rolling Stone* as the 'smartest indie-rock star of her generation'. Having studied at the prestigious Berklee College of Music, St. Vincent released her first solo album in 2007. After wide critical acclaim, she has gone on to produce another four albums that have received various accolades. In 2014, her fourth studio album *St. Vincent* won a Grammy for Best Alternative Music Album, making St. Vincent the first woman in more than two decades to receive the award. She has even invented her own line of guitars, which are specifically designed for women's bodies, to empower girls and women to feel more comfortable when playing.